Japanese Test Book

Prepares the learner for high school and college

Listening comprehension questions

Applies variety of testing methods

Answer keys included

The Adventure Begins...

SpeedSpeak
JAPANESE

by

D.H. Groberg

Test Book

TEST TAKING INSTRUCTIONS

The purpose of these tests is to facilitate your learning and remembering the material covered in SpeedSpeak Japanese. They form an integral part of the course and should not be skipped. They are designed to reinforce the learning as well as identify what you might need to review again. We want you to do well on each test. Don't hesitate to review and take the test again if you want to.

TO GAIN THE MAXIMUM BENEFIT FROM YOUR SPEED SPEAK JAPANESE COURSE, PLEASE FOLLOW THE TEST INSTRUCTIONS CAREFULLY.

The more senses we use to learn something, the more easily we will learn and recall what we have learned. These tests are designed to use as many of your senses as possible to reinforce your learning. We first ask you to say it out loud which gives you practice speaking and feeling (almost tasting) the words in your mouth. As you speak you can hear the sounds. As you hear the sounds, you can almost feel them in your mind. Next, as you write, you use your eyes and hands (using the sense of sight, hand-eye coordination and your motor skills). This writing reinforces again what you have said and heard. Then we ask you to say the phrase or answer again to further reinforce the learning. Altogether this process insures that your learning will be fast, fun, and effective.

Each test consists of five steps. Each steps should be completed in sequence. By completing all five steps in sequence, you will learn the material faster, you will speak more accurately, it will be more enjoyable for you, and you will remember the material much better. Here are the five steps:

1. Saying the test answer out loud.

2. Writing the answer in the box or lines provided.

3. Saying the answer out loud again.

4. Checking your answers to see how many were correct.

5. Recording your scores on the Score Sheet.

Test One

Take this test by saying the answer out loud, then by writing the answer in the box, and then by saying it out loud again.

(1) What is a simple "Good morning"?

> *(Say it out loud)*

(2) A more polite "Good morning"?

> *(Say it out loud)*

(3) What is "Hello" or "Hi"? (Greeting during the day.)

> *(Say it out loud)*

(4) How about "Good evening"?

> *(Say it out loud)*

(5) How do you say "Good night"?

> *(Say it out loud)*

Now go to the Answer Section in the Test Book to check your answers.

Test Two

Take this test by saying the answer out loud, then by writing the answer in the box, and then by saying it out loud again.

(6) "Please" (go ahead, etc.)

(Say it out loud)

(7) "After you, please"

(Say it out loud)

(8) "Thank you"

(Say it out loud)

(9) "I'm sorry" or "excuse me"

(Say it out loud)

(10) "How are you?"

(Say it out loud)

Now go to the Answer Section in the Test Book to check your answers.

Test Three

Take this test by saying the answer out loud, then by writing the answer in the box, and then by saying it out loud again.

(11) "Can do." "be able"

> (Say it out loud)

(12) "Can't do." "unable"

> (Say it out loud)

(13) "Japanese"

> (Say it out loud)

(14) "I can't speak Japanese"

> (Say it out loud)

(15) "English"

> (Say it out loud)

(16) "I can't speak English"

> (Say it out loud)

(17) Question marker

> (Say it out loud)

(18) "Can you speak English?"

> (Say it out loud)

(19) "I don't understand"

> (Say it out loud)

(20) "Don't you understand?"

> (Say it out loud)

Now go to the Answer Section in the Test Book to check your answers.

Test Four

Take this test by saying the answer out loud, then by writing the answer in the box, and then by saying it out loud again.

(21) "Please" (give me, or let me)

(Say it out loud)

(22) "Please write" (it down)

(Say it out loud)

(23) "Please read" (this)

(Say it out loud)

(24) "Telephone"

(Say it out loud)

(25) "Telephone me, please" (Give me a call)

(Say it out loud)

Now go to the Answer Section in the Test Book to check your answers.

Test Five

Take this test by saying the answer out loud, then by writing the answer in the box, and then by saying it out loud again.

Let's see how much you remember with looking back.

(1) "Good morning" (Simple)

(Say it out loud)

(2) "Good morning" (More polite)

(Say it out loud)

(3) "Hello" or "Hi"

(Say it out loud)

(4) "Good evening"

(Say it out loud)

(5) "Good night"

(Say it out loud)

(6) "Please" (go ahead, etc.)

(Say it out loud)

(7) "After you, please"

(Say it out loud)

(8) "Thank you"

(Say it out loud)

(9) "I'm sorry" or "excuse me"

(Say it out loud)

(10) "How are you?"

(Say it out loud)

(11) "Can do." "be able"

(Say it out loud)

(12) "Can't do." "unable"

(Say it out loud)

(13) "Japanese"

(Say it out loud)

(14) "I can't speak Japanese"

(Say it out loud)

(15) "English"

(Say it out loud)

(16) "I can't speak English"

(Say it out loud)

(17) Question marker

(Say it out loud)

(18) "Can you speak English?"

(Say it out loud)

(19) "I don't understand"

(Say it out loud)

(20) "Don't you understand?"

(Say it out loud)

Now go to the Answer Section in the Test Book to check your answers.

Test Six

Take this test by saying the answer out loud, then by writing the answer in the box, and then by saying it out loud again.

(26) "I'm hungry"

(Say it out loud)

(27) "Let's eat"

(Say it out loud)

(28) "Let's start eating" (For politeness)

(Say it out loud)

(29) "This tastes good"

(Say it out loud)

(30) "This tastes terrible"

(Say it out loud)

(31) "It's cold, isn't it?"

(Say it out loud)

(32) "It's hot, isn't it?"

(Say it out loud)

(33) "I like" (It, her, them, etc.)

(Say it out loud)

(34) "I don't want" (It, any, etc.)

(Say it out loud)

(35) "Water, please"

(Say it out loud)

Now go to the Answer Section in the Test Book to check your answers.

Test Seven

Take this test by saying the answer out loud, then by writing the answer in the box, and then by saying it out loud again.

(36) "Straight ahead"

> *(Say it out loud)*

(37) "Right, please"

> *(Say it out loud)*

(38) "Left, please"

> *(Say it out loud)*

(39) "Over there"

> *(Say it out loud)*

(40) "Right here"

> *(Say it out loud)*

Now go to the Answer Section in the Test Book to check your answers.

Test Eight

Take this test by saying the answer out loud, then by writing the answer in the box, and then by saying it out loud again.

(41) "Yes"

(Say it out loud)

(42) "No"

(Say it out loud)

(43) "Hey!" or "I say there" (Attention getter)

(Say it out loud)

(44) "Do you have(It)?" "Are there any?"

(Say it out loud)

(45) "Show me, please"

(Say it out loud)

(46) "Congratulations"

(Say it out loud)

(47) "(Are you) all right?" "O.K.?"

(Say it out loud)

(48) "When?"

(Say it out loud)

(49) "Right now!"

(Say it out loud)

(50) "Perhaps, maybe"

(Say it out loud)

Now go to the Answer Section in the Test Book to check your answers.

Test Nine

Take this test by saying the answer out loud, then by writing the answer in the box, and then by saying it out loud again.

(1) "Good morning" (Simple)

(Say it out loud)

(2) "Good morning" (More polite)

(Say it out loud)

(3) "Hello" or "Hi"

(Say it out loud)

(4) "Good evening"

(Say it out loud)

(5) "Good night"

(Say it out loud)

(6) "Please" (go ahead, etc.)

(Say it out loud)

(7) "After you, please"

(Say it out loud)

(8) "Thank you"

(Say it out loud)

(9) "I'm sorry" or "excuse me"

(Say it out loud)

(10) "How are you?"

(Say it out loud)

(11) "Can do." "be able"

(Say it out loud)

(12) "Can't do." "unable"

(Say it out loud)

(13) "Japanese"

(Say it out loud)

(14) "I can't speak Japanese"

(Say it out loud)

(15) "English"

(Say it out loud)

(16) "I can't speak English"

(Say it out loud)

(17) Question marker

(Say it out loud)

(18) "Can you speak English?"

(Say it out loud)

(19) "I don't understand"

(Say it out loud)

(20) "Don't you understand?"

(Say it out loud)

(21) "Please" (give me, or let me)

(Say it out loud)

(22) "Please write" (it down)

(Say it out loud)

(23) "Please read" (this)

(Say it out loud)

(24) "Telephone"

(Say it out loud)

(25) "Telephone me, please" (Give me a call)

(Say it out loud)

(26) "I'm hungry"

(Say it out loud)

(27) "Let's eat"

(Say it out loud)

(28) "Let's start eating" (For politeness)

(Say it out loud)

(29) "This tastes good"

(Say it out loud)

(30) "This tastes terrible"

(Say it out loud)

(31) "It's cold, isn't it?"

(Say it out loud)

(32) "It's hot, isn't it?"

(Say it out loud)

(33) "I like" (It, her, them, etc.)

(Say it out loud)

(34) "I don't want" (It, any, etc.)

(Say it out loud)

(35) "Water, please"

(Say it out loud)

(36) "Straight ahead"

(Say it out loud)

(37) "Right, please"

(Say it out loud)

(38) "Left, please"

(Say it out loud)

(39) "Over there"

(Say it out loud)

(40) "Right here"

(Say it out loud)

(41) "Yes"

(Say it out loud)

(42) "No"

(Say it out loud)

(43) "Hey!" or "I say there" (Attention getter)

(Say it out loud)

(44) "Do you have(It)?" "Are there any?"

(Say it out loud)

(45) "Show me, please"

(Say it out loud)

(46) "Congratulations"

(Say it out loud)

(47) "(Are you) all right?" "O.K.?"

(Say it out loud)

(48) "When?"

(Say it out loud)

(49) "Right now!"

(Say it out loud)

(50) "Perhaps, maybe"

(Say it out loud)

Now go to the Answer Section in the Test Book to check your answers.

Answer Keys

Answer keys to the Japanese tests and Japanese Comprehension tests.

Answers to Test One

How well did you do? Check your answers now.

(1) | "Good morning" (simple) | = | OHIO. |

(2) | "Good morning" (more polite) | = | OHIO GOES EYE-MOSS. |

(3) | "Hello" or "Hi" | = | KONE KNEE CHEE WAH. |

(4) | "Good evening" | = | COMB BON WAH. |

(5) | "Good night" | = | OH YAH SUE ME. |

Now record your score here.

This test had 5 possible correct answers. Record your score here _____. If you got fewer than 4 of the answers correct, go back and review the material again and take this test again before you proceed to the next section of Module one.

Answers to Test Two

How well did you do? Check your answers now.

(6) | "Please" (go ahead, etc.) | = | DOZO.

(7) | "After you, please" | = | O SOCKIE KNEE DOZO.

(8) | "Thank you" | = | ODDIE GOT TOE.

(9) | "I'm sorry" or "excuse me" | = | SUE ME MOSS END.

(10) | "How are you?" | = | OH-GAIN KEY?

Now record your score here.

This test had 5 possible correct answers. Record your score here _____. If you got fewer than 4 of the answers correct, go back and review the material again and take this test again before you proceed to the next section of Module one.

Answers to Test Three

How well did you do? Check your answers now.

(11)	"Can do." "be able"	=	DAY KEY MOSS.
(12)	"Can't do." "unable"	=	DAY KEY MOSS "N".
(13)	"Japanese"	=	KNEE HONE GO.
(14)	"I can't speak Japanese"	=	KNEE HONE GO DAY KEY MOSS "N".
(15)	"English"	=	"A" GO.
(16)	"I can't speak English"	=	"A" GO DAY KEY MOSS "N".
(17)	Question marker	=	CAW.
(18)	"Can you speak English?"	=	"A" GO DAY KEY MOSS CAW?
(19)	"I don't understand"	=	WAH CODDY MOSS "N".
(20)	"Don't you understand?"	=	WAH CODDY MOSS "N" CAW?

Now record your score here.

This test had 10 possible correct answers. Record your score here _____. If you got fewer than 8 of the answers correct, go back and review the material again and take this test again before you proceed to the next section of Module one.

Answers to Test Four

How well did you do? Check your answers now.

(21) | "Please" (give me, or let me) | = | COO DAH SIGH.

(22) | "Please write" (it down) | = | KITE TEH COO DAH SIGH.

(23) | "Please read" (this) | = | YONE DAY COO DAH SIGH.

(24) | "Telephone" | = | DEN WAH.

(25) | "Telephone me, please" | = | DEN WAY COO DAH SIGH.

Now record your score here.

This test had 5 possible correct answers. Record your score here _____. If you got fewer than 4 of the answers correct, go back and review the material again and take this test again before you proceed to the next section of Module one.

Answers to Test Five

How well did you do? Check your answers now.

(1) | "Good morning" (simple) | = | OHIO.

(2) | "Good morning" (more polite) | = | OHIO GOES EYE-MOSS.

(3) | "Hello" or "Hi" | = | KONE KNEE CHEE WAH.

(4) | "Good evening" | = | COMB BON WAH.

(5) | "Good night" | = | OH YAH SUE ME.

(6) | "Please" (go ahead, etc.) | = | DOZO.

(7) | "After you, please" | = | O SOCKIE KNEE DOZO.

(8) | "Thank you" | = | ODDIE GOT TOE.

(9) | "I'm sorry" or "excuse me" | = | SUE ME MOSS END.

(10) | "How are you?" | = | OH-GAIN KEY?

(11) | "Can do." "be able" | = | DAY KEY MOSS.

(12) | "Can't do." "unable" | = | DAY KEY MOSS "N".

Answers to Test Five (continued)

(13) | "Japanese" | = | KNEE HONE GO.

(14) | "I can't speak Japanese" | = | KNEE HONE GO DAY KEY MOSS "N".

(15) | "English" | = | "A" GO.

(16) | "I can't speak English" | = | "A" GO DAY KEY MOSS "N".

(17) | Question marker | = | CAW.

(18) | "Can you speak English?" | = | "A" GO DAY KEY MOSS CAW?

(19) | "I don't understand" | = | WAH CODDY MOSS "N".

(20) | "Don't you understand?" | = | WAH CODDY MOSS "N" CAW?

Now record your score here.

This test had 20 possible correct answers. Record your score here _____. If you got fewer than 16 of the answers correct, go back and review the material again and take this test again before you proceed to Module Two.

Answers to Test Six

How well did you do? Check your answers now.

Here's what you should have sid for each of the phrases about eating.

(26) | "I'm hungry" | = | O KNOCK A SWEET TAH.

(27) | "Let's eat" | = | TUB "A" MOSS SHOW.

(28) | "Let's start eating" (For politeness) | = | EAT TAH DOCKY MOSS.

(29) | "This tastes good" | = | O. E. SHE.

(30) | "This tastes terrible" | = | MA ZOOIE.

(31) | "It's cold, isn't it?" | = | SAW MOOIE NEIGH.

(32) | "It's hot, isn't it?" | = | HOT SUEY NEIGH.

(33) | "I like" (It, her, them, etc.) | = | SKI DES.

(34) | "I don't want" (It, any, etc.) | = | E. D. MOSS "N".

(35) | "Water, please" | = | OH ME ZOO COO DAH SIGH.

Now record your score here.

This test had 10 possible correct answers. Record your score here _____. If you got fewer than 8 of the answers correct, go back and review the material again and take this test again before you proceed to the next section of Module Two.

Answers to Test Seven

How well did you do? Check your answers now.

(36) | "Straight ahead" | = | MOSS SUE GOO.

(37) | "Right, please" | = | ME-GOO COO DAH SIGH.

(38) | "Left, please" | = | HE DODDY COO DAH SIGH.

(39) | "Over there" | = | AH SOAK "O".

(40) | "Right here" | = | COCO.

Now record your score here.

This test had 5 possible correct answers. Record your score here _____. If you got fewer than 4 of the answers correct, go back and review the material again and take this test again before you proceed to the next section of Module Two.

Answers to Test Eight

How well did you do? Check your answers now.

(41) | "Yes" | = | HIGH. |

(42) | "No" | = | "E" YEA. |

(43) | "Hey!" or "I say there" | = | ON "O" NEIGH. |

(44) | "Do you have(It)?" "Are there any?" | = | ODDY MOSS CAW? |

(45) | "Show me, please" | = | ME SET "A" COO DAH SIGH. |

(46) | "Congratulations" | = | OH MED-EH-TOE. |

(47) | "(Are you) all right?" "O.K.?" | = | DIE JOE BOO DES CAW. |

(48) | "When?" | = | EAT SUE? |

(49) | "Right now!" | = | "E" MAW. |

(50) | "Perhaps, maybe" | = | TAW BOONE. |

Now record your score here.

This test had 10 possible correct answers. Record your score here _____. If you got fewer than 8 of the answers correct, go back and review the material again and take this test again before you proceed to the final test of Module Two.

Answers to Test Nine

How well did you do? Check your answers now.

(1)	"Good morning" (simple)	=	OHIO.
(2)	"Good morning" (more polite)	=	OHIO GOES EYE-MOSS.
(3)	"Hello" or "Hi"	=	KONE KNEE CHEE WAH.
(4)	"Good evening"	=	COMB BON WAH.
(5)	"Good night"	=	OH YAH SUE ME.
(6)	"Please" (go ahead, etc.)	=	DOZO.
(7)	"After you, please"	=	O SOCKIE KNEE DOZO.
(8)	"Thank you"	=	ODDIE GOT TOE.
(9)	"I'm sorry" or "excuse me"	=	SUE ME MOSS END.
(10)	"How are you?"	=	OH-GAIN KEY?
(11)	"Can do." "be able"	=	DAY KEY MOSS.
(12)	"Can't do." "unable"	=	DAY KEY MOSS "N".
(13)	"Japanese"	=	KNEE HONE GO.
(14)	"I can't speak Japanese"	=	KNEE HONE GO DAY KEY MOSS "N".
(15)	"English"	=	"A" GO.
(16)	"I can't speak English"	=	"A" GO DAY KEY MOSS "N".

Answers to Test Nine (continued)

(17) | Question marker | = | CAW.

(18) | "Can you speak English?" | = | "A" GO DAY KEY MOSS CAW?

(19) | "I don't understand" | = | WAH CODDY MOSS "N".

(20) | "Don't you understand?" | = | WAH CODDY MOSS "N" CAW?

(21) | "Please" (give me, or let me) | = | COO DAH SIGH.

(22) | "Please write" (it down) | = | KITE TEH COO DAH SIGH.

(23) | "Please read" (this) | = | YONE DAY COO DAH SIGH.

(24) | "Telephone" | = | DEN WAH.

(25) | "Telephone me, please" | = | DEN WAY COO DAH SIGH.

(26) | "I'm hungry" | = | O KNOCK A SWEET TAH.

(27) | "Let's eat" | = | TUB "A" MOSS SHOW.

(28) | "Let's start eating" (For politeness) | = | EAT TAH DOCKY MOSS.

(29) | "This tastes good" | = | O. E. SHE.

(30) | "This tastes terrible" | = | MA ZOOIE.

(31) | "It's cold, isn't it?" | = | SAW MOOIE NEIGH.

(32) | "It's hot, isn't it?" | = | HOT SUEY NEIGH.

(33) | "I like" (It, her, them, etc.) | = | SKI DES.

(34) | "I don't want" (It, any, etc.) | = | E. D. MOSS "N".

Answers to Test Nine (continued)

(35) | "Water, please" | = | OH ME ZOO COO DAH SIGH.

(36) | "Straight ahead" | = | MOSS SUE GOO.

(37) | "Right, please" | = | ME-GOO COO DAH SIGH.

(38) | "Left, please" | = | HE DODDY COO DAH SIGH.

(39) | "Over there" | = | AH SOAK "O".

(40) | "Right here" | = | COCO.

(41) | "Yes" | = | HIGH.

(42) | "No" | = | "E" YEA.

(43) | "Hey!" or "I say there" | = | ON "O" NEIGH.

(44) | "Do you have(It)?" "Are there any?" | = | ODDY MOSS CAW?

(45) | "Show me, please" | = | ME SET "A" COO DAH SIGH.

(46) | "Congratulations" | = | OH MED-EH-TOE.

(47) | "(Are you) all right?" "O.K.?" | = | DIE JOE BOO DES CAW.

(48) | "When?" | = | EAT SUE?

(49) | "Right now!" | = | "E" MAW.

(50) | "Perhaps, maybe" | = | TAW BOONE.

Now record your score here.

This test had 50 possible correct answers. Record your score here _____. If you got fewer than 40 of the answers correct, go back and review the material again and take this test again before you proceed.

Japanese Test 12

Tape 3, Side A

Name _____

A. MATCHING

Instructions: Match the following Japanese phrases with the correct English equivalent.

1. _____ *Sayonara*
2. _____ *Ikimashou*
3. _____ *douzo*
4. _____ *shirimasen*
5. _____ *eigo*
6. _____ *nihongo*
7. _____ *sumimasen*
8. _____ *kore*
9. _____ *doumo arigatou*
10. _____ *amerikajin*
11. _____ *atama*
12. _____ *me*
13. _____ *hitobito*
14. _____ *demo*
15. _____ *kowai*

a. I don't know
b. thank you
c. Japanese
d. American
e. let's go
f. pardon me
g. head
h. good-bye
i. frightening
j. this
k. people
l. English
m. but
n. go ahead
o. eye

B. TRANSLATION

Instructions: Translate these Japanese phrases into English.

16. *Eigo (ga) wakarimasu ka.*

_____.

17. *sumimasen*

_____.

18. *Tanaka desu.*

_____.

19. *Amerikajin desu ka.*

_____.

20. *Naoko wa tomodachi desu ka.*

_____.

21. *te*

_____.

22. *Raion wa hashirimasen.*

_____.

23. *Tanaka-san wa keeki o tsukurimasu.*

_____.

24. *san*

_____.

C. TRANSLATION

Instructions: Translate these Japanese phrases into English.

25. *Kore wa nan desu ka.*

_____.

26. *Nihongo de _____ wa nan desu ka.*

_____.

27. *kuchi*

_____.

28. *kao*

_____.

29. *Ashi ga arimasu ka.*

_____.

30. *Kenji wa keeki o tsukurimasu.*

_____.

31. *Usagi wa nemasu.*

_____.

32. *rokusen*

_____.

33. *Naomi wa tomodachi deshou.*

_____.

D. RESPONSES

Instructions: Write the correct responses (in Japanese) to these expressions.

34. *Ashita tesuto o ukemasu.*

_____.

35. *Doumo arigatou gozaimasu.*

_____.

36. *Omedetou gozaimasu.*

_____.

37. *Yoroshiku onegai shimasu.*

_____.

38. *Ame ga furisou desu.*

_____.

39. *Shitsumon ga arimasu.*

_____.

40. *Douzo, go-enryo naku.*

_____.

41. *Omatsuri ni ikimasu.*

_____.

42. *Tasukete kudasatte arigatou gozaimashita.*

_____.

E. READ AND DRAW

Instructions: Read the following phrases. Then draw what they describe.

43. *isses*   44. *niten*

45. *goten to nisen*

46. *sansen to rokuten*

47. *yonten to ichi to san*

48. *nisen to roku*

49. *niten to sansen*

50. *roku, go, yon, san, ni, ichi*

Japanese Test 13

Tape 3, Side B

Name _____

A. MATCHING

Instructions: Match these Japanese phrases with the correct English equivalent.

1. _____ *ookii*		a. this, it
2. _____ *chiisaii*		b. skillful
3. _____ *kore*		c. but
4. _____ *sore*		d. singing
5. _____ *to*		e. big
6. _____ *mo*		f. black
7. _____ *demo*		g. that
8. _____ *ringo*		h. where
9. _____ *kuroi*		i. one (thing in general)
10. _____ *shiroi*		j. small
11. _____ *doko ni*		k. play the guitar
12. _____ *hitotsu*		l. also
13. _____ *jouzu*		m. white
14. _____ *gitaa o hiku*		n. and
15. _____ *utau koto*		o. apple

B. TRANSLATION

Instructions: Translate these Japanese phrases into English.

16. *Dare ga utatte iru?*

_____.

17. *yori*

_____.

18. *itsumo*

_____.

19. *foukusongu*

_____.

20. *soretomo*

_____ .

21. *akai ringo*

_____ .

22. *kiiroi pen*

_____ .

23. *chiisai naifu*

_____ .

24. *betsu no pen*

_____ .

25. *Kono pen wa akai desu.*

_____ .

C. TRANSLATION

Instructions: Translate these Japanese expressions into English.

26. *Kore wa kuroi pen desu.*

_____ .

27. *Akai pen arimasu ka.*

_____ .

28. *Sore wa chiisai naifu desu.*

_____ .

29. *Ookii naifu wa koko ni arimasu.*

_____ .

30. *Kore wa chiisai naifu desu ka.*

_____ .

31. *Iie, sore wa ookii naifu desu.*

_____ .

32. *Kore wa kiiroi pen desu ka.*

_____ .

33. *Hai, sore wa kiiroi pen desu.*

_____ .

34. *Betsu no pen arimasu ka.*

_____ .

35. *Hai, akai pen mo arimasu.*

_____ .

D. NUMBERS

Instructions: Write out the Japanese way of expressing the following numbers.

36. 420

_____.

37. 635

_____.

38. 1240

_____.

39. 5000

_____.

40. 750

_____.

41. 8000

_____.

42. 10000

_____.

E. READING COMPREHENSION

Instructions: Read the following conversation. Then answer the questions based on the reading.

Conversation at a Royal Ball

1: *Konbanwa!*

2: *A--! Konbanwa!*

1: *Ima, dare utatte imasu ka.*

2: *Oujo desu.*

1: *Itsumo akai ringo o taberu oujo desu ka.*

2: *Iie. Kono oujo wa gitaa o hikimasu. Kono oujo wa ringo o taberu oujo
no oneesan desu.*

1: *Gitaa o hiku oujo wa utau de jouzu desu ne.*

2: *Sou desu ne.*

1: *Ringo o taberu oujo ga utaimasu ka.*

2: *Iie, utaimasen. Kedo piano o hikimasu.*

1: *Sou desu ka. Ja, ouji wa nani o shimasu ka.*

2: *Ouji wa kiiroi ringo o tabemasu.*

43. Who is singing?

a. a king

b. a queen

c. a princess

d. a prince

44. True or false: The singing princess likes to eat yellow apples.

45. True or false: The singing princess plays the guitar.

46. Is the singing princess the older sister of the princess who eats apples?

47. What instrument does the apple-eating princess play?

a. piano

b. flute

c. guitar

d. tuba

48. What color apples does the younger princess eat?

a. yellow

b. red

c. green

d. fluorescent pink

49. Is the guitar-playing princess good at singing?

50. What is the prince doing?

a. eating red apples

b. playing the guitar

c. standing on his head

d. eating yellow apples

Japanese Test 14

Tape 4, Side A

Name _____

A. MATCHING

Instructions: Match the following English words with the correct Japanese equivalent.

1. _____ book   a. *kagi*
2. _____ chair   b. *doushite*
3. _____ exactly   c. *ie*
4. _____ brick   d. *isu*
5. _____ table   e. *sanbiki no buta*
6. _____ key   f. *renga*
7. _____ park   g. *chigai*
8. _____ house   h. *hon*
9. _____ room   i. *wara*
10. _____ happy   j. *teeburu*
11. _____ three pigs   k. *fukuro*
12. _____ straw   l. *kouen*
13. _____ difference   m. *sono touri*
14. _____ bag   n. *ureshii*
15. _____ why   o. *heya*

B. TRANSLATION

Instructions: Translate these Japanese phrases into English.

16. *Dare wa utau no ga suki ja nai?*

_____.

17. *Oujo wa utau no ga suki desu ka.*

_____.

18. *Inu to neko wa utau no ga heta?*

_____.

19. *Utau no wa kekkou jouzu.*

_____.

20. *Kore wa watashi no kiiroi enpitsu desu.*

_____.

21. *Kurata-san wa shiroi kami o motte imasu ka.*

_____.

22. *Yamada-san wa akai pen o motte imasu.*

_____.

23. *Mariko wa ningyou.*

_____.

24. *Oukami wa wara no ie ni kuru.*

_____.

25. *Hon o teeburu no ue ni tatete kudasai.*

_____.

C. TRANSLATION

Instructions: Translate these Japanese expressions into English.

26. *Hon o motte imasu ka.*

_____.

27. *Teeburu no ue ni oite kudasai.*

_____.

28. *Nihongo o benkyou shite imasu.*

_____.

29. *Sono touri ni iimashita.*

_____.

30. *Chiisai buta no wara no ie wa fukitobu.*

_____.

31. *Mariko no kao o mite.*

_____.

32. *Dono joou?*

_____.

33. *Kore wa watashi no shiroi kami desu.*

_____.

34. *Dono oujo to dono ouji to?*

_____.

35. *Emiko wa gitaa o hiku koto ga suki desu.*

_____.

D. RESPONSES

Instructions: Write the correct responses (in Japanese) to these expressions.

36. *Osoku natte kimashita ne.*

_____.

37. *Nomimono onegai shimasu.*

_____.

38. *Tetsudaimashou ka.*

_____.

39. *Kono kotoba no imi ga wakarimasen.*

_____.

40. *Douzo, osaki ni.*

_____.

41. *Kouen o sanpou shimashou.*

_____.

42. *Zenbu jibun de shimashita.*

_____.

Japanese Test 15

Tape 4, Side B

Name _____

A. MATCHING

Instructions: Match the following English words with the correct Japanese equivalent.

1. _____ moon		a. *konkai*
2. _____ Friday		b. *tsuyoi*
3. _____ acquaintance		c. *chijin*
4. _____ cousin		d. *hako*
5. _____ today		e. *tsuki*
6. _____ this time		f. *kyou*
7. _____ box		g. *subarashii*
8. _____ great		h. *nagai*
9. _____ long		i. *itoko*
10. _____ strong		j. *kinyoubi*

B. TRANSLATION

Instructions: Translate these Japanese phrases into English.

11. *Kyou wa totemo tanoshikatta desu.*

_____.

12. *Tasukete kudasatte arigatou gozaimasu.*

_____.

13. *Tashika ni watashi ga machigatte imashita.*

_____.

14. *Yagyuu-san mo enpitsu o motte imasu ka.*

_____.

15. *Enpitsu o kudasai.*

_____.

16. *Kono hoka no fukuro ni enpitsu ga arimasu.*

_____.

17. *Ima yoku mite.*

_____.

18. *Kuroi enpitsu wa chiisai hako ni arimasu.*

_____.

19. *Hanashinagara, wara ga aru torakku ni iru otoko no hito o mita.*

_____.

20. *Sanbiki no buta wa renga no ie ni nagai aida shiawase ni sunda.*

_____.

C. TRANSLATION

Instructions: Translate these Japanese expressions into English.

21. *Ushi wa tsuki o tonda koto to iwarete imasu.*

_____.

22. *Shinjiraremasen!*

_____.

23. *Wakarimashita.*

_____.

24. *Shirane-san wa watashi no chijin desu.*

_____.

25. *Dou iu fuu ni?*

_____.

26. *Kiiroi kami wa doko ni arimasu ka.*

_____.

27. *Sore nara watashi no poketto ni aru no wa aoi enpitsu deshou?*

_____.

28. *Mukashi, mukashi, sanbiki no buta ga ita.*

_____.

29. *Kyoudai datta, shikashi, seikaku wa chigatta.*

_____.

30. *Shikashi, chiisai buta wa nibanme no buta no ie ni hashitta.*

_____.

D. RESPONSES

Instructions: Write the correct responses (in Japanese) to these expressions.

31. *Dekimasen!*

_____.

32. *Kinyoubi made ikemasen.*

_____.

33. *Moshi moshi. Fukuman-san wa irasshaimasu ka.*

_____.

34. *Kurogi-san wa watashi no chijin desu.*

_____.

35. *Sumimasen kedo ima ikanakute wa narimasen.*

_____.

36. *Tashika ni watashi ga machigatte imashita.*

_____.

37. *Ohisashiburi desu ne.*

_____.

38. *Shitsurei shimashita.*

_____.

39. *Ikanakereba narimasen.*

_____.

40. *Subarashii desu ne.*

_____.

Japanese Test 16

Tape 5, Side A

Name _____

A. MATCHING

Instructions: Match the following English words with the correct Japanese equivalent.

1. _____ time   a. *neko*
2. _____ five-minute break   b. *poketto*
3. _____ trust   c. *mijikai*
4. _____ anytime   d. *gofun no kyuukei*
5. _____ patience   e. *chuugoku*
6. _____ China   f. *kuruma*
7. _____ absolutely   g. *noujou*
8. _____ short   h. *shinrai*
9. _____ cat   i. *mori*
10. _____ farm   j. *mochiron*
11. _____ Spanish   k. *kuma*
12. _____ car   l. *jikan*
13. _____ pocket   m. *gaman*
14. _____ bear   n. *supeingo*
15. _____ woods   o. *itsudemo*

B. TRANSLATION

Instructions: Translate these Japanese phrases into English.

16. *Gohan wa sugoku atsui.*

_____.

17. *Onna no ko ga mori no naka o aruku.*

_____.

18. *Kuma wa isu o miru.*

_____.

19. *Aoi enpitsu to akai pen wa fukuro no naka ni arimasu.*

_____.

20. Nakunatta no desu ka.

_____.

21. Nandai kuruma o omochi desu ka.

_____.

22. Totemo okanemochi desu ne.

_____.

23. Oikutsu desu ka.

_____.

24. Otousan wa doko desu ka.

_____.

25. Me o tojite, oboete mite.

_____.

C. TRANSLATION

Instructions: Translate these Japanese expressions into English.

26. Donata desu ka.

_____.

27. Ikimashou.

_____.

28. Hontou ni moushiwake arimasen.

_____.

29. Sorekara dou shimasu ka.

_____.

30. Kono kikai wa nani o shimasu ka.

_____.

31. Akai mono no hanbun ika ga mijikai desu.

_____.

32. Hanbun ijou ga nagai desu.

_____.

33. Hotondo wa nagai desu.

_____.

34. Tawaa de ou-sama to joou-sama to utatte iru.

_____.

35. Mama to papa wa Afurika ni sunde iru?

_____.

D. RESPONSES

Instructions: Write the correct responses (in Japanese) to the following expressions.

36. *Watashitachi to issho desu ka.*

_____.

37. *Jikan ga amari arimasen.*

_____.

38. *Tsukaremashita. Mou dame desu.*

_____.

39. *Kore wa nani ni tsukaimasu ka.*

_____.

40. *Itsu soko ni tsukimasu ka.*

_____.

Japanese Test 17

Tape 5, Side B

Name _____

A. MATCHING

Instructions: Match the following English words with the correct Japanese equivalent.

1. _____ comfortable
2. _____ chair
3. _____ bedroom
4. _____ bowl
5. _____ broken
6. _____ someone
7. _____ wonderful
8. _____ summer
9. _____ spring
10. _____ April
11. _____ to remember
12. _____ thumb
13. _____ mistake
14. _____ Italian
15. _____ library

a. *haru*
b. *isu*
c. *oboeru*
d. *kowareta*
e. *itariago*
f. *subarashii*
g. *oyayubi*
h. *donburi*
i. *toshokan*
j. *raku*
k. *shigatsu*
l. *dareka*
m. *machigai*
n. *shinshitsu*
o. *natsu*

B. TRANSLATION

Instructions: Translate these Japanese phrases into English.

16. *Mukashi, mukashi santou no kuma ga ita.*

_____.

17. *Chiisaii isu ni suwaru.*

_____.

18. *Nyuushou shimashita.*

_____.

19. *Hai, ima omoi dashimashita.*

_____.

20. *Teeburu no ue ni iroiro na renga ga arimasu.*

_____.

21. *Watashitachi no ashi o mite.*

_____.

22. *Uso o tsukanaide.*

_____.

23. *Supeingo ka doitsugo o hanashimasu ka.*

_____.

C. TRANSLATION

Instructions: Translate the following Japanese expressions into English.

24. *Doushite mo nemasu.*

_____.

25. *Eigo wa sekaijuu de hanasarete imasu deshou?*

_____.

26. *Watashi mo sou omoimasu.*

_____.

27. *Dekiru to omoimasu.*

_____.

28. *Akachan no yubi o mite.*

_____.

29. *Kono renga o torimasu.*

_____.

30. *Dou yatte kono biru ni hairemashita ka.*

_____.

31. *Santou no kuma wa shinshitsu ni hairu.*

_____.

D. RESPONSES

Instructions: Write the correct responses (in Japanese) to these expressions.

32. *Nyuushou shimashita.*

_____.

33. *Ani wa watashi ni okotte imasu.*

_____.

34. *Doko ni ikimashou ka.*

_____.

35. *Koko kara toui desu ka.*

_____.

36. *Doushite mo nemasu.*

_____.

37. *Kore wa kitto anata niwa dekimasen!*

_____.

38. *Tanaka to mou shimasu. Douzo yoroshiku onegai shimasu.*

_____.

39. *Eigo o hanashimasu ka.*

_____.

40. *Kore wa ikura desu ka.*

_____.

Japanese Test 18

Tape 6, Side A

Name _____

A. MATCHING

Instructions: Match the following English words with the appropriate Japanese equivalent.

1. _____ both   a. *zenbu*
2. _____ all   b. *nikai*
3. _____ same   c. *mado*
4. _____ total   d. *kemuri*
5. _____ ruler   e. *michi*
6. _____ street   f. *ryouhou*
7. _____ window   g. *hanashi*
8. _____ picture   h. *ki*
9. _____ story   i. *goukei*
10. _____ roof   j. *doa*
11. _____ smoke   k. *yane*
12. _____ door   l. *jougi*
13. _____ sky   m. *onaji*
14. _____ tree   n. *sora*
15. _____ second floor o. *e*
16. _____ master   p. *entotsu*
17. _____ orange   q. *kowareta*
18. _____ chimney   r. *shujin*
19. _____ end   s. *owari*
20. _____ broken   t. *orenji*

B. TRANSLATION

Instructions: Translate these Japanese phrases into English.

21. *Ikutsu ka mono o agemashou.*

_____.

22. *Nagai shiroi bou to mijikai akai bou.*

_____.

23. *Nonbon no tanzaku?*

_____.

24. *Jougi wa nani iro desu ka.*

_____.

25. *Goukei juunihon deshou?*

_____.

26. *Zenbu kiiro desu.*

_____.

C. TRANSLATION

Instructions: Translate the following Japanese expressions into English.

27. *Zenbu de gohon no bou--nagai no wa san bon to mijikai no wa nihon.*

_____.

28. *Juuni-inchi no jougi.*

_____.

29. *Dakara zenbu de juunihon no mono o motte imasu.*

_____.

30. *Zenbu de nanbon no enpitsu to bou?*

_____.

31. *Juunihon no uchi, nanbon ga kiiro desu ka.*

_____.

32. *Enpitsu wa nani iro desu ka.*

_____.

D. OPPOSITES

Instructions: Write the opposite for each of the following Japanese words.

33. *chikai*   _____
34. *nagai*   _____
35. *chiisaii*   _____
36. *jouzu*   _____
37. *shiroi*   _____
38. *atsui*   _____

Japanese Test 19

Tape 6, Side B

Name _____

A. MATCHING

Instructions: Match the following English words with the correct Japanese equivalent.

1. _____ today
2. _____ Thursday
3. _____ explain
4. _____ plan
5. _____ school
6. _____ train
7. _____ professor
8. _____ far
9. _____ why
10. _____ bus
11. _____ Monday
12. _____ bike

a. *mokuyoubi*
b. *toui*
c. *gakkou*
d. *getsuyoubi*
e. *kyou*
f. *basu*
g. *kyouju*
h. *setsumei suru*
i. *jitensha*
j. *densha*
k. *naze*
l. *keikaku*

B. TRANSLATION

Instructions: Translate the following English sentences into Japanese.

13. Repeat, please, in a bit louder voice.

_____.

14. I've been studying English for many years.

_____.

15. Are you going with us?

_____.

16. Why are you laughing?

_____.

17. You can't take pictures here.

_____.

C. TRANSLATION

Instructions: Translate the following Japanese sentences into English.

18. *Doko ni ikimashou ka.*

_____.

19. *Koko ni dono gurai irassaimasu ka.*

_____.

20. *Sore wa watashi no inu dewa arimasen.*

_____.

21. *Iie, zettai ni hontou desu yo.*

_____.

22. *Zutsuu ga shimasu.*

_____.

D. RESPONSES

Instructions: Write the correct responses (in Japanese) to these expressions.

23. *Sumimasen, wakarimasen deshita.*

_____.

24. *Watashi wa nihongo ga totemo heta desu.*

_____.

25. *Chotto matte kudasai!*

_____.

26. *Ano tesuto wa totemo muzukashikatta desu.*

_____.

27. *Chigau densha ni notte imasu yo.*

_____.

Japanese Comprehension Tests

Listen to the following words and phrases. Each will be repeated three times. Translate them into English. Then listen to a narrative in Japanese, which will be repeated two times. As you listen to the story a second time, make your notes more complete.

WORDS AND PHRASES

1. _____
2. _____
3. _____
4. _____
5. _____
6. _____
7. _____
8. _____
9. _____
10. _____
11. _____
12. _____
13. _____
14. _____
15. _____
16. _____
17. _____
18. _____
19. _____
20. _____
21. _____
22. _____
23. _____
24. _____
25. _____
26. _____
27. _____
28. _____
29. _____
30. _____
31. _____
32. _____

NARRATIVE

Answer Keys

Here are the answers for the Japanese Tests.

Japanese Test 12

Tape 3, Side A

A. MATCHING

1. h 2. e 3. n 4. a 5. l 6. c 7. f 8. j
9. b 10. d 11. g 12. o 13. k 14. m
15. i

B. TRANSLATION

16. Do you understand English?
17. Pardon me. 18. I am Tanaka.
19. Are you an American? 20. Naoko is a
girl. 21. hand 22. The lion doesn't run.
23. Mr. Tanaka eats cake. 24. three

C. TRANSLATION

25. What is this? 26. What is ____ in
Japanese? 27. mouth(s) 28. face(s)
29. Do you have feet? 30. Kenji makes
cakes. 31. The rabbit sleeps. 32. six
lines 33. Naomi is a friend, right?

D. RESPONSES

34. *Ganbatte kudasai!* 35. *Dou
itashimashite.* 36. *Arigatou gozaimasu.*
37. *Kochira koso.* 38. *Sou desu ne.*
39. *Nan desu ka.* 40. *Itadakimasu.*
41. *Watashi mo ikimasu.* 42.
Tondemonai desu.

E. READ AND DRAW

43. ____   44. • •
45. • • • • • ____ ____
46. ____ ____ ____ ____
47. • • • • & 1 & 3
48. ____ ____ & 6
49. • • ____ ____ ____

50. 6, 5, 4, 3, 2, 1

Japanese Test 13

Tape 3, Side B

A. MATCHING

1. e 2. j 3. a 4. g 5. n 6. l 7. c 8. o
9. f 10. m 11. h 12. i 13. b 14. k
15. d

B. TRANSLATION

16. Who is singing? 17. more than
18. always 19. folksongs 20. or 21. red
apple(s) 22. yellow pen(s) 23. small knife
24. another pen 25. This pen is red.

C. TRANSLATION

26. This is a black pen. 27. Is there a red
pen? 28. That is a small knife. 29. The
big knife is here. 30. Is this a small knife?
31. No, that is a big knife. 32. Is this a
yellow pen? 33. Yes, that is a yellow pen.
34. Is there another pen? 35. Yes, there
is also a red pen.

D. NUMBERS

36. *yonhyaku nijuu* 37. *roppyaku sanjuu
go* 38. *sen nihyaku yonjuu* 39. *gosen*
40. *nanahyaku gojuu* 41. *hassen* 42.
man

E. READING COMPREHENSION

43. c 44. false 45. true 46. yes 47. a
48. b 49. yes 50. d

Japanese Test 14

Tape 4, Side A

A. MATCHING

1. h 2. d 3. m 4. f 5. j 6. a 7. l 8. c
9. o 10. n 11. e 12. i 13. g 14. k
15. b

B. TRANSLATION

16. Who doesn't like to sing?
17. Does the princess like to sing?
18. Do the dog and cat sing poorly?
19. Their singing is pretty skillful.
20. This is my yellow pencil.
21. Does Mr. Kurata have white paper?
22. Ms. Yamada has a red pen.
23. Mariko (is) a dolly. 24. The wolf comes to the house of straw. 25. Stand the book up on the table.

C. TRANSLATION

26. Do you have a book? 27. Put it on the table, please. 28. I'm studying Japanese. 29. That's just what I said.
30. The little pig's house of straw falls.
31. Look at Mariko's face. 32. Which queen? 33. This is my white paper. 34. With which princess and which princess?
35. Emiko likes to play the guitar.

D. RESPONSES

36. *Ee, kaerimashou.* 37. *Hai, wakarimashita.* 38. *Iie, daijoubu desu.*
39. *Watashi mo wakarimasen.* 40. *Hai. Sumimasen.* 41. *Oukee, sou shimashou.*
42. *Yoku dekimashita.*

Japanese Test 15

Tape 4, Side B

A. MATCHING

1. e 2. j 3. c 4. i 5. f 6. a 7. d 8. g
9. h 10. b

B. TRANSLATION

11. Today was very fun. 12. Thank you for helping me. 13. I was definitely mistaken. 14. Does Mr. Yagyuu also have a pencil? 15. Give me a pencil.
16. In this other sack there is a pencil. 17. Now watch attentively. 18. The black pencil is in the small box. 19. As they were talking, they saw a man in a truck with a load of straw. 20. The three little pigs lived happily in the house of bricks for many years.

C. TRANSLATION

21. It's said that a cow jumped over the moon. 22. Incredible! 23. Understood.
24. Mr. Shirane is an acquaintance of mine. 25. In what way? 26. Where is the yellow paper? 27. Then it is the blue pencil that is in my pocket, right?
28. There were once three pigs.
29. They were brothers, but they had different characters. 30. But the little pig went running to the house of the second little pig.

D. RESPONSES

31. *Dekimasu yo. Ganbatte kudasai.*
32. *Watashi mo.* 33. *Dochirasama desu ka.* 34. *Watashi wa shirimasen.* 35. *Mata kite kudasai.* 36. *Shitte iru beki deshita.* 37. *Hontou ni.* 38. *Daijoubu desu. Yoku aru koto desu kara.* 39. *Sabishiku narimasu.* 40. *Sou desu ne. Subarashii desu.*

Japanese Test 16

Tape 5, Side A

A. MATCHING

1. l 2. d 3. h 4. o 5. m 6. e 7. i 8. c
9. a 10. g 11. n 12. f 13. b 14. k
15. i

B. TRANSLATION

16. The food is very hot. 17. A girl walks through the woods. 18. The bears see the chairs. 19. The blue pencil and the red pen are inside the bag. 20. Is it gone? 21. How many cars do you have? 22. You must be very rich. 23. How old are you? 24. Where is your father? 25. Close your eyes and try to remember.

C. TRANSLATION

26. Who are you? 27. Let's go. 28. I'm very sorry. 29. And then what? 30. What does this machine do? 31. Less than half of the red things are short. 32. More than half are long. 33. Most are long. 34. They are singing with the king and queen in the tower. 35. Do Mama and Papa live in Africa?

D. RESPONSES

36. *Hai, issho desu.* 37. *Goshinpai naku, jikan wa juubun arimasu.* 38. *Jaa, gofun kyuukei shimashou.* 39. *Seikaku niwa nanto itte ii ka wakarimasen.* 40. *Gaman shite, sugu tsukimasu yo.*

Japanese Test 17

Tape 5, Side B

A. MATCHING

1. j 2. b 3. n 4. h 5. d 6. l 7. f 8. o
9. a 10. k 11. c 12. g 13. m 14. e
15. i

B. TRANSLATION

16. There once were three bears. 17. She sits down on the little chair. 18. I won the prize. 19. Yes, now I remember. 20. On the table there are various bricks. 21. Look at our feet. 22. Don't tell lies. 23. Do you speak Spanish or German?

C. TRANSLATION

24. No matter what, I'm going to sleep. 25. English is spoken all around the world, right? 26. I think so, too. 27. I think I can do it. 28. Look at baby's fingers. 29. I take this brick. 30. How were you able to enter this building? 31. The three bears go into the bedroom.

D. RESPONSES

32. *Omedetou.* 33. *Sore wa mata doushite?* 34. *Oishii resutoran o shitte imasu.* 35. *Iie, touku arimasen. Totemo chikai desu.* 36. *Oyasumi nasai.* 37. *Yarasete kudasai.* 38. (student's name) *to mou shimasu. Douzo yoroshiku onegai shimasu.* 39. *Mochiron.* 40. *Hyaku doru.*

Japanese Test 18

Tape 6, Side A

A. MATCHING

1. f   2. a   3. m   4. i   5. l   6. e   7. c   8. o
9. g   10. k   11. d   12. j   13. n   14. h
15. b   16. r   17. t   18. p   19. s   20. q

B. TRANSLATION

21. I'll give you several things.
22. A long white rod and a short red rod.
23. How many strips of paper?   24. What color is the ruler?   25. A total of twelve things, right?   26. All are yellow.

C. TRANSLATION

27. In all, five rods: three long and two short   28. A twelve-inch ruler.   29. So in all you have twelve things.   30. In all, how many pencils and rods?   31. Of your twelve things, how many are yellow?
32. The pencils are what color?

D. OPPOSITES

33. *toui*   34. *mijikai*   35. *ookii*   36. *heta*
37. *kuroi*   38. *samui*

Japanese Test 19

Tape 6, Side B

A. MATCHING

1. e   2. a   3. h   4. l   5. c   6. j   7. g   8. b
9. k   10. f   11. d   12. i

B. TRANSLATION

13. *Mou ichido, onegai shimasu, mou sukoshi ookina koe de.*   14. *Eigo o nannen no benkyou shite imasu.*
15. *Watashitachi to issho ni ikimasu ka.*
16. *Naze waratte imasu ka.*   17. *Koko ni shashin o toremasen.*

C. TRANSLATION

18. Where shall we go?   19. How long have you been here?   20. That isn't my dog.   21. No, it's absolutely true.   22. I have a headache.

D. RESPONSES

23. *Dewa, mou ichido setsumei shimasu.*
24. *Sonna koto nai desu yo!*
25. *Dekimasen. Isoide imasu kara.*
26. *Sou deshita ne.*   27. *Hontou desu ka. Kore wa doko e ikimasu ka.*

Japanese Comprehension Test

WORDS AND PHRASES

1. Good morning (more polite) 2. Hello or Hi 3. Good evening 4. Good night
5. After you, please 6. I'm sorry or Excuse me 7. How are you? 8. Yes, thanks 9. I can't speak Japanese
10. Can you speak English? 11. I don't understand 12. Please write (it down)
13. Please read (this) 14. Telephone me please (Give me a call) 15. I'm hungry
16. Let's eat 17. Let's start eating (A polite phrase said before eating) 18. This tastes good (Delicious) 19. It's hot, isn't it? 20. I like (I like it, or I like her, etc.)
21. I don't want it. 22. Water please
23. Straight ahead 24. Left 25. Right
26. Here 27. Do you have it, or Are there any? 28. Show me please
29. Congratulations 30. Are you all right? 31. When? 32. Now

FOREIGN
LANGUAGE COURSES

PN 3639-01